Doonesbury
by GB Trudeau.

Foreword by Erich Segal

Library of Congress Catalog Card
Number: 76-142978

07-065294-5

234567890 HDEC 75432

To Annie,
who only likes a few of them

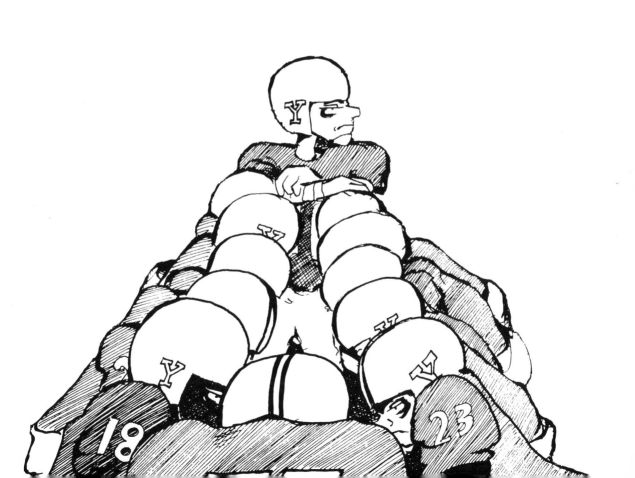

Foreword

by Erich Segal

There is an ulterior motive to my writing these words for the initial volume of the *Compleat Workes of Garry Trudeau*. Simply stated, I would like the world to know that Garry was once a student of mine at Yale. This might suggest that I am in some way responsible for Trudeau's comic genius and thereby attract the interest of future biographers, thesis writers, and (hopefully) groupies.

Now there is a certain truth in my statement.

Garry Trudeau actually did take my course.

But that's all. As far as who taught whom, it's quite another matter. *I* learned from Garry.

What I know about campus sex, drugs, radicals, and crazies I learned from Garry Trudeau.

I also know that if the previous sentence is ever quoted out of context I may be out of a job. But the truth must be served.

Of course you readers understood at once that I got my education from Garry's *cartoons*. Right? I think it was Voltaire who said that comedy provided the best of all possible mirrors to the life it mocked. Anyway, it bears repeating: we discover today's college young in Trudeau's mirror.

Moreover, Trudeau sees the campus and its divers denizens as people —not merely raw material for comic distortion. His technique is not gross hyperbole, but graceful epitome. He reduces life to its essential foibles. We laugh because what he shows us is so true, but more important, we smile because he has been so gentle. We are grateful that he prefers wisecrack to slapstick. We wouldn't want anyone to get hurt—especially us. For we are his subjects, as are all the funny little fragile people —even the football players.

One of the most common put-downs of today's young people is that they lack a sense of humor. Humbug. Garry Trudeau is an original comic talent who can bring smiles to both overbearing parents and ungrateful kids. He is neither Disney nor Feiffer; he is uniquely himself. Which, by the way, is the definition of a real artist.

And remember, I said it first.

Ezra Stiles College
Yale University
November, 1970

Doonesbury

ALRIGHT, GUYS, THIS IS THE FIRST DAY OF PRACTICE, SO I'M SURE ALL OF YOU ARE UNDERSTANDABLY NERVOUS. SO I THOUGHT WE'D WARM UP WITH AN OLD FAVORITE PLAY OF MINE, THE "CLEVELAND CLUTCH."

O.K. NOW, THIS IS THE WAY THE "CLEVELAND CLUTCH" WORKS... THE FRONT LINE THROWS UP A GOOD BLOCK. THE ENDS RUN STRAIGHT DOWN THE FIELD, AND YOU BACKS TEAR OFF AROUND THE ENDS.

I'LL EITHER PASS DOWNFIELD, OR ROLL OUT TO ONE OF THE BACKS, OR I'LL RUN THE BALL MYSELF, OR MAYBE I'LL JUST PUNT.

ACTUALLY, THE "CLEVELAND CLUTCH" IS A VERY FLEXIBLE PLAY.

GBTrudeau

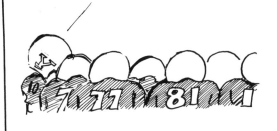

Doonesbury

WELL, I LET YOU GUYS TAKE THE LAST PLAY AND WHAT HAPPENED? YOU BUTCHERED IT! YOUR BIG CHANCE FOR YOU ALL TO MAKE IT WITHOUT ME AND YOU BLEW IT!

YOU ALL REPEATEDLY REFUSE TO RUN THESE PLAYS RIGHT. YOU FORCE ME TO DO ALL THE SCORING! NONE OF YOU HAVE ONE OUNCE OF SPEED, ENDURANCE OR BRAINS! IN FACT, WHAT DOES ONE OF YOU HAVE THAT I DON'T HAVE MORE OF? HUH? WHAT?

SOUL, BABY.

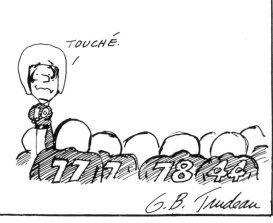

TOUCHÉ.

G.B. Trudeau

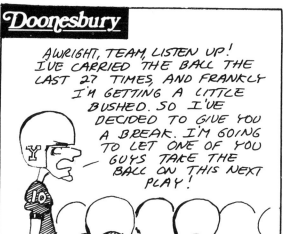

Doonesbury

O.K., GUYS, THIS IS MY LAST PLAY THIS GAME. THAT LAST PLAY I BROKE MY LEG, AND THE COACH SAYS I'VE GOTTA REST UP. BUT I JUST WANT YOU ALL TO KNOW THAT IT'S BEEN SWELL PLAYING BALL WITH YOU THIS GAME...

...SO AT LEAST FOR NOW, SO LONG, FELLAS

GODDAMNIT, B.D., WE'RE GOING TO MISS YOU!!

ACTUALLY, IT'S VERY RARE THAT YOU GET SUCH "PIGSKIN PATHOS" FROM A 260 LB. FULLBACK.

G.B. Trudeau

Doonesbury

DESPITE PREVIOUS FAILURES AT THIS MIXER TONITE, MIKE "THE MIX," INEXPERIENCED BUT EAGER FRESHMAN, STILL LOOKS AROUND FOR HIS FIRST SCORE OF THE EVENING.

SPOTTING A YOUNG LOVELY HE APPROACHES HER..

HI THERE! HOW ABOUT A LITTLE DANCE?

SURE, YOU GROSS SKINNY LITTLE FROSH!

HA HA HA HA HA

IF I WEREN'T SO SKINNY AND LITTLE, I'D RAPE HER FOR THAT.

AH HA HA HA HA

GB Trudeau

Doonesbury

YOU KNOW, B.D., YOU REALLY DID LOOK KIND OF SILLY WALTZING INTO BRIARCLIFF WITH YOUR FOOTBALL HELMET ON.

YOU KNOW, IN THE LONG RUN, YOU'RE ONLY MAKING THINGS TOUGHER FOR YOURSELF. WHY DO YOU HAVE TO WEAR YOUR HELMET? I MEAN, WHY DO IT?

BECAUSE IT'S PART OF MY **GODDAMN LIFE STYLE**, THAT'S WHY!

TOUCHY.

G. B. Trudeau

Doonesbury

HAVING SPOTTED THE FUZ OUTSIDE THE HOUSE, "MEGAPHONE" MARK IS UNDERSTANDABLY NERVOUS WHEN HE HEARS A KNOCK ON THE DOOR...

KNOCK!

KNOCK!

EXCUSE ME, ARE YOU "MEGAPHONE" MARK?

YUP. UH-HUH.

PSST...

WHAT A GAS. HEH-HEH. GET IT?

GB Trudeau

Doonesbury

GB Trudeau

Doonesbury

IT'S MORE KUDOS FOR YALE'S YOUTHFUL PRESIDENT AS HE STARTS OUT ON HIS MORNING WALK THROUGH THE COLLEGES TO REDUCE TENSIONS CAUSED BY THE HARVARD INCIDENT. ...AH THE DEAN APPROACHETH...

WELL, GOOD MORNING, GEORGE! AS YOU CAN WELL SEE, YOU'VE CAUGHT ME ON MY MORNING STROLL AMONG THE STUDENTS, RELIEVING TENSIONS AND TALKING OUT THE ISSUES.

THAT'S FINE, KING, REAL FINE. BUT GUESS WHO JUST TOOK OVER YOUR HOUSE AS YOU'VE BEEN STROLLING AMONG THE STUDENTS?

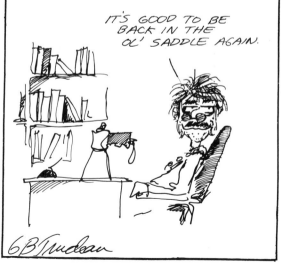

IT'S GOOD TO BE BACK IN THE OL' SADDLE AGAIN.

GBTrudeau

Doonesbury

WELL, HERE I AM ON A TRAIN TO CAMBRIDGE AFTER MY RELEASE ON BAIL. OH, WOW, DO I HATE FUZZ!

BUT I'LL MAKE THEM PAY! RIGHT NOW I'M ON MY WAY TO HARVARD TO HELP OUT MY SDS BRETHREN... I'M GOING TO BE AN *OUTSIDE AGITATOR*!

WAIT'LL THE BOSTON GLOBE GETS THE STORY: "*MEGAPHONE MARK ARRIVES AT HARVARD TO AID REBELS' CAUSE!*" OH, MAN, WHEN THEY SEE THE HAVOC I'LL CAUSE, THE FUZZ WILL REGRET THE DAY THEY RELEASED ME FROM JAIL!

OF COURSE, THEY MAY ALREADY BE ON TO ME...

GBTrudeau

Doonesbury

O.K., NOW COMES THE PAYOFF PLAY!! I CALL IT THE "OHIO EXPRESS." THE FRONT LINE THROWS UP A GOOD BLOCK. I FADE BACK TO OUR OWN 5 YARD LINE.

WAITING UNTIL AT LEAST THREE MEN ARE UPON ME, BALANCING ON ONE FOOT, I THROW AN UNDERHAND 95 YARD SPIRAL WHICH I'LL RUN DOWN AND CATCH ON THE GOAL LINE. O.K. BREAK!!

RIGHT.

G. B. Trudeau

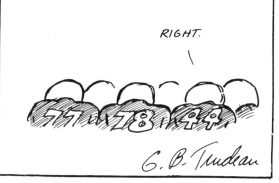

Doonesbury

Doonesbury

IT'S ANOTHER LONELY NIGHT FOR LONESOME LINDA LOCAL, PERT ELEVENTH-GRADER AT DAY PROSPECT, AS SHE CRUISES THROUGH THE OLD CAMPUS AREA LOOKING FOR A NICE YALE MALE WHO WILL TREAT HER KIND...

DESPITE HER NEAT NEW BLACK PEA JACKET AND JAZZY BELLBOTTOM JEANS, THE FELLAS ARE PASSING LONESOME LINDA BY, NOT REALIZING THAT SHE TOO IS A WARM HUMAN BEING.

THERE GOES ANOTHER ONE.. I GUESS I MIGHT AS WELL FACE IT, THERE JUST AREN'T ANY YALIES SO HARD UP THEY WANT TO GET INVOLVED WITH A NICE LOCAL GIRL...

HI, THERE! MY NAME'S MIKE!

LET ME QUALIFY THAT...

G B Trudeau

Doonesbury

EVEN THOUGH I NOW ENTER MY SECOND DAY OF SUSPENSION, I FEEL A TREMENDOUS SENSE OF RELIEF. MY WHOLE BODY TELLS ME, "MEGAPHONE MARK, YOU SUSPENDED STUD, WHAT A SENSE OF RELIEF. NO MORE RESPONSIBILITIES AT ALL!"

FOR WITH SUSPENSION HAS COME FREEDOM! AT LAST I AM **FREE** FROM THE SHACKLES OF MY PAST. I AM MY OWN MAN. THE LAST TWO DAYS OF BEING FREE HAVE BEEN BLISS.... AH, A LETTER...

YALE STATION

"GREETINGS..."

YALE STATION

SO MUCH FOR MY PERIOD OF GRACE....

YALE STATION

GB Trudeau

Doonesbury

ENTER ARNIE HOLTBERG, THE PRINCETON KICKER WHO JUST LOST THE GAME TO YALE. AS HE WALKS INTO HIS EATING CLUB, HE IS SURE TO BE GREETED BY HIS FRIENDS IN THE USUAL *PRINCETON* MANNER....

NONETHELESS, HE IS NOT ALL THAT WORRIED THAT HIS FRIENDS WILL REALLY REJECT HIM...

BOO!

HISS!

BOO!

BOO, ARNIE!

HEH, HEH, DON'T WORRY, ARNOLD, WE'RE JUST RIBBING YOU, KID!

CE NE FAIT RIEN, OL' MAN. COME ON OVER AND HAVE A FEW DRINKS!

...WE ALL PREPPED TOGETHER.

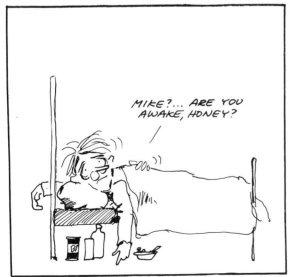

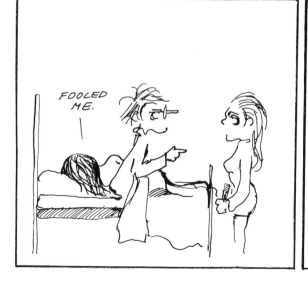

Panel 1:
HERE I AM ONCE AGAIN AT THE STATION, WAITING FOR AN OLD FLAME, MILDRED, TO ARRIVE ON THE NOON BUS. BOY! TALK ABOUT EXCITEMENT.

BUS STOP

Panel 2:

OL' MILLIE CERTAINLY WAS EXCITED WHEN I CALLED HER UP AND INVITED HER FOR A COLLEGE WEEKEND. I'LL BET SHE'D BEEN PINING AWAY FOR ME, CRYING HERSELF TO SLEEP, ALL THE WHILE THINKING, "MIKE, DEAR MIKE! HOW I LOVE THEE, MIKE!

RALPH!

STOP

Panel 3:

RALPH! HOW ARE YOU, RALPH! HOW DIVINE TO SEE YOU AGAIN!

BUS STOP

Panel 4:

NOT RALPH, EH? DICK, IT'S DICK, ISN'T IT? NO? HOW ABOUT BILL, WILLY? NO, DON'T TELL ME, IT'S NICK, RIGHT? NO...

BUS STOP

GBTrudeau

WELL, HERE I AM AT THE ROTC RECRUITING CENTER. ANXIOUS TO AVOID THE DRAFT, I HAVE WISELY SIGNED UP FOR THE CONCENTRATED INTENSIVE FOUR WEEK ROTC CRASH COURSE OFFERED TO SENIORS.

SO YOU'RE IN THE ARMY NOW, EH, MARK, KID? WELL, IT'S NOT ALL GOING TO BE ROSES, I CAN PROMISE YOU THAT! WE'RE GOING TO BE ASKING YOU TO GIVE EVERY PART OF YOUR BODY AND MIND TO BEING THE BEAUTIFUL CREATURE THAT IS A SOLDIER.

BUT THAT DOESN'T MEAN THERE ARE NO REWARDS! HELL, NO! YOU'LL REALIZE THE WARM FEELING OF CHOWING DOWN WITH THE GUYS, YOU'LL COME TO LOVE THE ACRID, BITTERSWEET SMELL OF GUNPOWDER AND SWEATY LEATHER, YOU'LL TREMBLE WITH PRIDE EACH TIME YOU HEAR THE BUGLE CALL YOU TO FALL IN! KID, WELCOME ABOARD! WE'RE GLAD TO HAVE YOU!

I THINK I'M GOING TO THROW UP.

GBTrudeau

Doonesbury

I'D LIKE TO THANK YOU, **CATHY**, FOR COMING TO DINNER. WE'RE MEETING THIS GUY FROM TRUMBULL CALLED **SAM SMOOTH** — HE APPARENTLY GIVES LESSONS IN **SEDUCING WOMEN!** NATURALLY, I'M A BIT INTERESTED, BUT I WANT TO KNOW WHAT YOU AS A GIRL THINK OF HIM....

FRANKLY MIKE, I'VE NEVER HEARD OF ANYTHING SO TOTALLY AB....

HULLO. YOU MUST BE MIKE. MY NAME IS SAM SMOOTH.

WHAT ARE YOUR RATES, SAM?

GBTrudeau

Doonesbury

OH, NO, IT'S THE BLACK PANTHERS SELLING IN FRONT OF LIGGETT'S. WELL, I'VE HAD ENOUGH OF *THEIR* NEWSPAPERS!! THIS TIME THEY'RE **NOT** GOING TO INTIMIDATE ME.

OKAY, HOLD IT RIGHT THERE, MEN. I'M NOT "CHECKING OUT" ONE MORE PAPER! WHY SHOULD I? THE MONEY GOES TO THE REVOLUTION, **RIGHT**? I'D BE NAILING MY OWN COFFIN! NO, SIR, **NOT FOR ME!**

YOU SAY YOU'RE *AGAINST* OUR FREE BREAKFAST PROGRAM FOR CHILDREN?

..AND ANOTHER WHITE LIBERAL HITS THE DUST...

GBTrudeau

Doonesbury

MAY I HAVE YOUR ATTENTION, PLEASE? TODAY IN AMERICAN STUDIES 34-B, WE HAVE A SPECIAL GUEST LECTURER...

I'M SURE YOU ARE ALL CONCERNED ABOUT THE PROBLEMS BLACK PANTHERS ARE FACING TODAY IN THIS COUNTRY. I KNOW I AM.

I THINK IT'S IMPORTANT THAT WE ALL KNOW THE PANTHER SIDE OF THE STORY. NOW I HAVE A FRIEND WHO SAID HE COULD GET ME ONE FOR MY CLASS. NEEDLESS TO SAY, *I WAS THRILLED!*

SO HERE HE IS, AN ACTUAL *BLACK PANTHER!!*

YEA! YEA!

CLAP CLAP

RIGHT ON!

CLAP CLAP

Doonesbury

GOOD EVENING, I'M HARRY REASONER AND I'M HERE IN NEW HAVEN WHERE THE ACTION IS. . . .

HERE IN NEW HAVEN, THERE ARE SMALL STUDENTS, THERE ARE BIG STUDENTS. BUT THEY HAVE ONE THING IN COMMON— THEY HATE OPPRESSION. I'M ABOUT TO INTERVIEW ONE SUCH. . . .

SURE, HARRY, YOU GREASY, ESTABLISHMENT, PATRONIZING, SELF-CONSCIOUSLY LIBERAL, CONDESCENDING, MEDIA FREAK.

HARRY REASONER, CBS NEWS, NEW HAVEN.